BY YOUR SIDE

A Guide for Caring for the Dying at Home

Barbara Karnes, RN

Book and cover design by Elemental (elemental.love)

Barbara Karnes Books, Inc
P.O. Box 822139
Vancouver, WA 98682
Phone 360-828-7132
Fax 360-828-7142
www.bkbooks.com

BY YOUR SIDE

A Guide for Caring for the Dying at Home

Barbara Karnes, RN

Contents

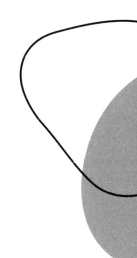

V. DEMENTIA

VI. CAREGIVER SELF CARE
Be Gentle With Yourself
Laughter Heals
Taking on the Distress
Adequate Rest
Getting Out and About
Accept Help
Find a Listener
Nutrition
Write Everything Down
Emotions/Pre-Grief
At the End of the Day
The Gift

EPILOGUE

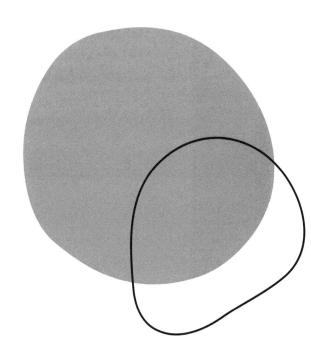

Introduction

Taking care of someone as the end of their life approaches is not the same as taking care of someone who is going to get better. Added to the potent mixture of fear, uncertainty, and lack of sleep is "early" grieving. We begin to mourn the loss of someone we love before they die. The care, medications, and outcomes are different as well. And, maybe most importantly, few of us have been involved in caring for someone who is dying. Movies and television show us death, but it is generally misrepresented. We just don't know what it is like to die, or what to do when someone is dying.

Our strongest emotion when life has tasked us with caring for someone who is dying is FEAR. It is overwhelming. Fear of the unknown, fear of making mistakes, fear of doing something we have never done before, fear of hurting our special person, fear of how death comes, fear of what to say, fear of what dying will look like, sound like, be like, and fear of what to do or not to do while it all is happening. Fear is the caregiver's companion most days. It is sometimes an unconscious fear but it influences all we see, feel, and think.

Having someone close to us in the dying process is so very sad but with a bit of knowledge it doesn't have to be a bad experience.

Knowledge reduces fear. Knowledge gives us the tools to do the work that needs to be done. Knowledge won't take away the sadness of losing a special person, but it will give you the confidence to know that you are providing the best possible care. This guidebook gives you that knowledge to support you through a very difficult and demanding time.

The journey of caring for your special person will be challenging and exhausting. My hope is that with this guidebook and the support of others (family, community, and professionals) this experience will be a special time for you that will become a sacred memory.

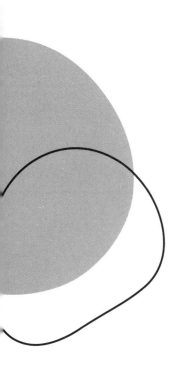

CHAPTER ONE

Choices

When a person is diagnosed with a life-threatening illness they are bombarded with new information. Their life has fundamentally changed and there are many decisions to be made. There are choices. This is when knowledge is your best friend, because the questions you ask and the answers you get will literally determine your future. This chapter provides references and guidance for making those choices.

Cure, Life Sustaining Care, or Comfort Care

The question everyone faced with a life threatening illness asks themselves is, "When do I stop seeking a cure, or life sustaining care, and accept comfort care?" First, let's define cure, life sustaining care, and comfort care:

A **Cure** provides a return to a functioning life. It implies being able to address, partake, and enjoy the activities of living.

Life sustaining care means keeping the physical body alive in whatever manner that is deemed necessary—including the use of artificial feeding, machines (ventilators, dialysis, respirators), and/or advanced medical procedures.

Comfort Care focuses on the quality of life being lived, as opposed to concentrating on the lengthening of life no matter the quality. Comfort care is good physical body care (addresses discomforts, hygiene, activity issues). Comfort care is emotional, mental, and spiritual support. Comfort care will address what is important to your well being now that your physical body is not meeting your needs. Comfort Care will guide and nurture those around you. Comfort care will encourage you and your family to live the best life you can within the confines of your disease. Comfort care is the focus of this guidebook.

For most people with a terminal illness a cure is unlikely. The question then becomes how much breathing do we want to do when we can't do much else. I know that sounds harsh, but I want to get your attention. Most life sustaining treatment is about keeping the lungs, kidneys, and heart functioning. What it isn't about is mobility, alert thinking, and independent living.

When it comes to making the choice between cure, life sustaining care, or comfort care, honest information and realistic knowledge is vital. We must ask these questions of our physician:

1) What is the projected outcome of my treatment?

2) How long will it take?

3) What will the quality of my life be with treatment (during and after)?

4) What will the quality of my life be without treatment?

Family will at some point be making the choices about how we will live the rest of our days. If there is no family, then the medical profession will make those choices for us—UNLESS we have in writing how we want to live until we are dead.

Family members have the most difficult time letting a loved one die. It will never be okay for a mom or dad or anyone close to us to die. We want them where we can physically see them and touch them, even if they can't respond to us. Selfish, yes, but oh so human. One of the biggest gifts of love that we can give to those we care about is to tell them how we want to live until we are dead. Preferably before they need the information.

Just because we can do a medical procedure doesn't necessarily mean that it is in the best interest of the patient, and just because the medical establishment can't heal the physical body doesn't mean there isn't healing work left to do. There is still the healing of the mental, emotional, and spiritual parts of us. Dying isn't a medical event. It is so much more.

NOTES

Advance Directives, POLST

After our decision about how we want to approach the end of our life is made, we must share it with our family and physician, as well as put it in writing. There are a number of things that must be considered. These include:

Advance Directives: All adults, ill or not, should have an Advance Directive. It needs to include a person designated as having a Durable Medical Power of Attorney. An Advance Directive can be filled out at any time in your life and addresses issues that may arise in a medical situation.

It requires no medical personnel signatures and is not legally binding. You can Google "Advance Directives" (**aarp.org** has advance directive forms for each state), print out the form, fill it out, share it with important others, give a copy to and talk about it with your physician, and keep it in a handy place—done.

Physician Orders for Life Sustaining Treatment (POLST): A POLST is typically a short form with check marked questions that tell first responders and physicians what kind of life-sustaining treatment you wish to receive. Each state has its own version and they may go by slightly different names. You can get one from your doctor. It is a **legal, medical order** created for the seriously ill, frail, and elderly. It describes the kind of treatment or no treatment that is wanted in the event of a life threatening situation. POLST forms travel with you. They are completed by your health care provider after discussing what is important to you, your diagnosis, what is likely to happen in the future, and what your treatment options are. A doctor (sometimes physician assistant or nurse practitioner) **must** sign the POLST form for it to be valid. Using a POLST form can help legally ensure that our wishes are followed by medical professionals. An Advance Directive allows us to describe our wishes for end of life care but does not carry the force of law that a POLST does.

Because we all like to pretend that we are never going to die, Advance Directives are not made before they are needed. And when they are needed we are generally too sick to make rational decisions or, sometimes, even to be listened to and believed.

Medicine can prolong life but generally at the expense of our well-being. Or we can consider using medicine only as a tool to provide comfort, dignity, and support as our final life experience unfolds.

No Code/911

Allow Natural Death (AND), Do Not Attempt Resuscitation (DNAR), Do Not Resuscitate (DNR), No Code: AND, DNAR and DNR are basically all words for the same legal order, written or oral depending on the country, indicating that a person does not want to receive cardiopulmonary resuscitation (CPR) if that person's heart stops beating. Sometimes it also prevents other medical interventions.

The simplest explanation I found for "no code" was from the "Free Dictionary": "A note written in the patient record and signed by a qualified, usually senior or attending physician instructing the staff of the institution not to attempt to resuscitate a particular patient in the event of cardiac or respiratory failure. This instruction is usually given only when a patient is so gravely ill that death is imminent and inevitable."

When medical professionals determine that someone will die from their disease and that their body will stop functioning normally and only machines and severe medical interventions will sustain breathing, it is often asked if the person wants to be a no code and sign a DNR form. That means when the person stops breathing and/or their heart stops, medical professionals will NOT try to get the person breathing or try to restart the heart. They also will NOT use a lot of medications to keep the body functioning.

What most people don't realize is that when a person's heart stops and they are coded and it is a successful code (the heart is restarted) they will not be returning to a normal functioning life. Their previous condition will not be changed, let alone cured. In fact, there is often added to the already dire health crisis the addition of broken ribs.

Does having a POLST, DNR, and no code mean having no care at all? Definitely not. It means comfort care, which involves less medications and interventions that prolong being trapped in a non-working body. It places emphasis on allowing death to occur naturally following the body's timetable. It focuses on pain medicines, positioning, skin and mouth care, and family support.

In this age of advanced technology we tend to forget that everyone dies. We're born, we experience, we die. That is life. We have made amazing medical advances. We can prolong breathing, but with it generally comes suffering. And, of course, we will still eventually die.

Dying is not painful. Disease causes pain. The normal, natural way we die from disease or old age is we gradually withdraw, our sleeping increases, and we eat less and less. When the time comes that we actually stop breathing we are asleep and non-responsive.

Does choosing to be a "full code" (have everything medically possible done to keep you alive) buy more time? Maybe. But what kind of time? Unfortunately, it is generally not good, healthy, interactive time. Being a no code, and signing the DNR form does provide the assurance of a more comfortable, natural death.

There are questions to ask your physician when asked if you want to sign a DNR form, in other words, to become a no code. These are also the questions to ask if your loved one is in a medial situation and you are being asked to make these decisions because the person did not, and now cannot, address these issues:

1) What are my chances of returning to a "normal" life following my heart stopping and requiring the medical intervention to restart it?

2) Will the medical condition that stopped my heart and made me die be different (improved or declined) after you have restarted my heart?

3) What does a code involve? What will be done to my body?

4) If I choose to be a no code and to have a DNR order in my medical file, what will happen to me from now until I die? What kind of care will I receive? How will this decision affect my relationship with you, my doctor?

911: 911 is your "Help! I can't handle this alone" number to call for emergencies in the home. If you have a signed POLST or DNR form, you need to put it on your refrigerator for the first responders to see. If there is a medical emergency involving breathing or heart issues the paramedics will honor the POLST or DNR.

One of the advantages to being in hospice care or working with an End of Life Worker is you have someone to call when you need guidance, support, or help. It gives you an emergency contact other than 911.

> *Remember, the purpose of an Advance Directive is to have available our personal requests for medical treatment WHEN WE CANNOT speak for ourselves. An Advance Directive is only applicable when we are not capable of speaking for ourselves.*

Durable Medical Power of Attorney

There are two kinds of durable powers of attorney: one for finances, which lets you name someone to manage your financial affairs if you become incapacitated, and one for health care, which allows someone to make medical decisions for you.

With both powers of attorney you select a person to be your decision maker when you can no longer make decisions for yourself. This person needs to be someone who knows you well, your life style, beliefs, and what your wishes would be when facing life altering conditions. The durable medical power of attorney only conveys decision making privileges when the person can no longer speak for themself.

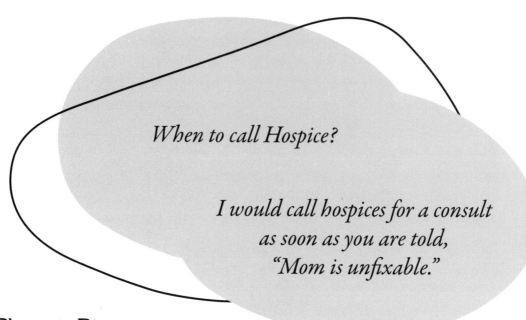

When to call Hospice?

*I would call hospices for a consult
as soon as you are told,
"Mom is unfixable."*

Places to Die

I think it is fair to say that most people would like to die at home with their family close and perhaps even their dog or cat on the bed. That seems like the ideal way to say goodbye.

Today. that is the least likely place we die. WHY? Several reasons:

1) It is hard work to care for the dying. It's an all day, all night job done by the people who care about us the most and who are therefore the most frightened and tired during this challenging time.

2) Our healthcare services (insurance, Medicare, Medicaid) do not offer enough comprehensive coverage to address all of the family's in-home care needs—being able to hire someone to assist the caregiver being a big uncovered need.

3) Most of us aren't given adequate referral time from our medical professionals to get in-home services in place and support given.

In the Hospital: Most people die in the hospital. To me, there is nothing comforting about a medical setting. There are rules, protocols, procedures, medical interventions, and certainly not a person's dog or cat on the bed. Hopefully, the family is given privacy, support of Chaplain services if wanted, and ongoing attention and guidance, but it is still a structured environment.

In a Nursing Home Facility: Nursing facilities are home to many people. Most facilities offer hospice services (their own, or they partner with outside agencies) to support and guide residents and their families through this life experience.

In a Hospice House: Another place people can die is in hospice facilities, often called Hospice Houses, which are medical facilities in a home-like setting. Staff is trained in end of life care and families have almost total freedom (kitchens to cook in, TV rooms, music rooms, quiet rooms, sleeping accommodations). A Hospice House is the next best thing to being at home. The family doesn't have the 24/7 responsibility of care, there is a limit to medical disruption, and you can even bring your own dog or cat.

If you say, "Yes, I want to go to a Hospice House," there are two catches: time and money. There is a limited time that you can be in a Hospice House under Medicare coverage. About a week or so is the reimbursed amount and then you must switch over to private pay. A good number of us do not have the funds required for several months of private pay and many Hospice Houses do not even offer it as an option.

At Home: Just like Dorothy says in **The Wizard of Oz**, "There is no place like home." You are in familiar surroundings. You set your own agendas and scheduling. You have your own visiting hours. You and your family are "in charge," set your own pace, answer to no one. Now add hospice or an End of Life Worker and you have professional support and guidance in your own surroundings.

Hospice care provides families with nursing visits, home health aide visits for bathing and bed changes, medical equipment like beds, wheelchairs, and commodes, counseling and support services, and volunteers to "patient sit" for a few hours of respite for the family caregivers. There is more, I've just named a few offerings. Hospice, when called in earlier than days before death, can set the stage for our "death of choice."

Help at Home

It used to be the word "hospice" was synonymous with the term "end of life care." Not so today. Today there are end of life doulas, death doulas, death midwives, transition volunteers, and No One Dies Alone volunteers. For simplicity I will refer to this entire group as End of Life (EOL) Workers.

A few EOL Workers work for hospice while others offer support and services independent of a hospice agency.

The majority of hospices in this country are Medicare certified. Meeting Medicare hospice guidelines makes them eligible for Medicare reimbursement. Services are provided to the patient at no charge because Medicare is "picking up the bill." Being certified also requires hospices to provide certain services. BUT, as with everything, just meeting requirements does not insure quality.

EOL Workers are often non-medical personnel. They are people who have been trained to address the support issues for the patient and family of someone with a life threatening illness. They have extensive knowledge in the physical, emotional, mental, spiritual and communal aspects of the dying process.

There are nurses, social workers, and chaplains who are EOL Workers, but it is not a requirement. There are many people interested in being of service at end of life who have taken one of the many courses and programs offered, are certified by that particular program, and offer their services as independent of any agency or hospital.

What is the difference between what hospice provides and what the EOL Workers provide? Hospice services are more medically oriented and are reimbursed by Medicare and most insurance policies. They also provide a variety of services that are non-medical.

A major difference between the two services is time. EOL Workers are generally not on the clock. They can stay for hours at a time. Part of their support is to be with the patient and family at the time of death as well as before and following. The services, however, are not reimbursed by Medicare or insurance carriers. You are responsible for their fees. Hospice services provide Registered Nurses, Licensed Practical Nurses, Certified Nurses Aides, Physical Therapists, Occupational Therapists, Social Workers, and Spiritual Counselors. It provides medical equipment (beds, commodes, wheelchairs) and pays for medications related to the terminal illness.

EOL Workers do not provide those services although they can guide you to getting them. These two approaches to end of life care are not opposed to each other. They compliment each other. I would like to see hospices hiring EOL Workers to fill the main gap in their services: time spent with families.

I suggest as a part of your Advance Directives you ask for the kind of funeral service you would like. Give yourself permission to "break the rules," to "think outside the box," to find a meaningful celebration of your life, of saying goodbye.

Funeral Planning

Making funeral arrangements says, "This is real. My special person is going to die." I think that is why we put off making them. BUT it needs to be done. Done before you need them.

Right now you are thinking about how your family will care for someone that has been told, "Go home, put your affairs in order, we can't fix you." Part of what needs to be done is funeral planning. Doing it before death comes avoids much confusion at a time when your heart will be screaming.

You need to know state laws and regulations regarding a death at home, funerals, and cremation. Do you need to call a coroner? What are funeral home protocols? Learn about cremation procedures. You need to learn about burying in cemeteries, burying outside cemeteries, in vaults, in mausoleums. What about a home funeral? You have to know your state laws and boundaries with funeral home policies.

Below is some general information but you need to be state specific and that will require research on your part. Hospice and/or an EOL Worker can help you with this information. A visit with a Funeral Director will also get you the needed information.

There are now Funeral Celebrants who will help you plan a funeral or memorial service.

The FTC Funeral Rule

The Funeral Rule, enforced by the Federal Trade Commission (FTC), makes it possible for you to choose only those goods and services you want or need. You pay only for those you select, whether you are making arrangements when a death occurs or in advance. The Funeral Rule allows you to compare prices among funeral homes. The Rule does not apply to third-party sellers, such as casket and monument dealers, or to cemeteries that lack an on-site funeral home.

The Funeral Rule gives you the right to:

• **Buy only the funeral arrangements you want.** You have the right to buy separate goods (such as caskets) and services (such as embalming or a memorial service). You do not have to accept a package that may include items you do not want. Things to do:

• **Get price information on the telephone.** Funeral directors must give you price information on the telephone if you ask for it. You don't have to give them your name, address, or telephone number first. Although they are not required to do so, many funeral homes mail their price lists, and some post them online.

• **Get a written, itemized price list when you visit a funeral home.** The funeral home must give you a General Price List (GPL) that is yours to keep. It lists all the items and services the home offers, and the cost of each one.

• **See a written casket price list before you see the actual caskets.** Sometimes detailed casket price information is included on the funeral home's GPL. More often, though, it's provided on a separate casket price list. Get the price information before you see the caskets, so that you can ask about lower-priced products that may not be on display.

• **See a written outer burial container price list.** Outer burial containers are not required by state law anywhere in the U.S., but many cemeteries require them to prevent the grave from caving in. If the funeral home sells containers, but doesn't list their prices on the GPL, you have the right to look at a separate container price list before you see the containers. If you don't see the lower-priced containers listed, ask about them.

• **Receive a written statement after you decide what you want, and before you pay.** It should show exactly what you are buying and the cost of each item. The funeral home must give you a statement listing every good and service you have selected, the price of each, and the total cost immediately after you make the arrangements.

• **Get an explanation in the written statement from the funeral home that describes any legal cemetery or crematory requirement** that obligates you to buy any funeral goods or services.

- **Use an "alternative container" instead of a casket for cremation.** No state or local law requires the use of a casket for cremation. A funeral home that offers cremations must tell you that alternative containers are available, and must make them available. They might be made of unfinished wood, pressed wood, fiberboard, or cardboard.

- **Provide the funeral home with a casket or urn you buy elsewhere.** The funeral provider cannot refuse to handle a casket or urn you bought online, at a local casket store, or somewhere else — or charge you a fee to do it. The funeral home cannot require you to be there when the casket or urn is delivered to them.

- **Make funeral arrangements without embalming.** No state law requires routine embalming for every death. Some states require embalming or refrigeration if the body is not buried or cremated within a certain time; some states don't require it at all. In most cases, refrigeration is an acceptable alternative. In addition, you may choose services like direct cremation and immediate burial, which don't require any form of preservation. Many funeral homes have a policy requiring embalming if the body is to be publicly viewed, but this is not required by law in most states. Ask if the funeral home offers private family viewing without embalming. If some form of preservation is a practical necessity, ask the funeral home if refrigeration is available. www.consumer.ftc.gov.

> *Ritual bathing is a way of saying goodbye through the hands and tears.*

Home Funerals

Home funerals with the body being bathed, dressed, cared for, watched over, and services all in the home are becoming more popular. It is more detailed than turning everything over to a funeral home BUT doing everything ourselves can also be a gift. Using our hands and our own energy is a way of channeling our grief and creating a ritual. If interested, check out **www.homefuneralalliance.org**.

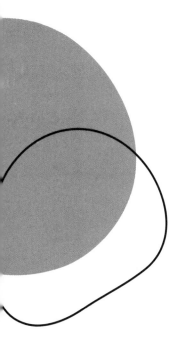

CHAPTER TWO

Approaching Death

We use the word "dying" to describe a process or a time period, but in that sense it is a misnomer. We are either alive or dead. The space inbetween is called living. Life is a terminal illness. We are "dying" all the time. We are born, we experience, and then we die. The only difference between someone in a healthy body and someone in an unhealthy body is that one of them is reminded every day they are not going to live forever.

No one knows how long life will be. Time is a gift most of us take for granted. Someone living in an unhealthy body has had their future taken away. They are forced to live in the present.

They have also had their purpose taken away. A future and a purpose go together. Most of us don't know how to live in the present. As people approach the end of their life we need to help them find a reason to get up in the morning. The physical body will die. The process by which it dies does not change. Understanding this process will help you determine what is normal and natural and what is out of the ordinary. What is okay and what you need help with. What requires medical assistance and intervention and what is just part of the normal way people die.

There are just two ways to die—fast or gradual. It is so simple. Fast death is getting hit by a car. It is a heart attack. It is suicide. You are alive one minute and dead the next.

Fast death is harder for the survivors than it is for the person who died. The survivors have unfinished business and unanswered questions. "What if?" "Why didn't I?" "If only?" Those questions and the ensuing guilt will complicate our grieving and make it more difficult.

Gradual death comes in two ways: old age and disease. In old age our body wears out and dies. With disease the body is killed by illness. The only difference between the two is time. A person who is old with no disease will take longer to die. They will have certain symptoms for years instead of months. A person who is old will have the signs of approaching death that signify weeks, last for months. When it gets down to days, hours, and minutes, we all die the same. You can also have a person dying from disease or old age who is alive one minute and dead the next, a fast death. They didn't play by the rules. But most people dying from disease or old age will predictably do certain things at certain times.

Gradual death gives us an opportunity to do and say those things we need to do and say. If we will take it. Most of us don't.

We don't even have to know a person's diagnosis to tell if they have entered the dying process. We don't have to know their lab values. All we have to do is ask questions concerning three pertinent areas—food, sleep, and social interaction. Based on the responses in these three areas we can tell if a person has months, weeks, days, or hours to live. Each person dies in their own unique manner. It will fit within a time frame, but the dynamics of their life determines that time frame, not lab values or diagnosis.

When we put a number on how long someone has to live we are doing that person a disservice. Because we don't know what it is like to die we think we are going to be alive one minute and dead the next. We don't know there is a process. Imagine the fear of waking up every morning and wondering if you are going to die that day. When I think that is happening I tell a person with a life threatening illness "If you can ask yourself 'Am I going to die today?' then you are probably not. The day that you die, you won't ask and you won't care." Think of the fear that that simple statement reduces.

An individual will die in their own unique way and time. They will probably do certain things within a certain time line but it will hold to their personality and the individual way they have lived their life. We die the same way that we have lived. Dying is just one more experience in life. We will deal with it in the same way that we have addressed all the other challenges.

We have limited control over the time that we die. That means we can choose to have someone with us when we die or we can protect a person by dying when they are not there.

There are few deathbed conversions. You don't generally go from being ornery and cantankerous to being a saint. What usually happens is you go from being ornery and cantankerous to being an absolute monster. Dying doesn't change us, it intensifies our personality.

A Type A, "doer" personality, will probably orchestrate their end of life. They may have their Advance Directive in place, their Durable Power of Attorneys, they may pick out their cemetery plot, may even write their own obituary. The Type A personality, may die more quickly than we expect. It would be intolerable for a Type A personality to be in bed for months.

Someone who is more laid back, a little easier going, content to watch television all afternoon, could develop a disease and die more slowly. There isn't a lot of difference between sitting in your favorite recliner or being in bed.

We all know people who use manipulation to get what they want in life. People can use manipulation in their dying as well. Take, for example, the mom who is dying. All of her adult kids are with her. "We'll stay with you as long as you need us," they tell her. Mom is not going to die quickly. She is probably getting more attention from her children in this dying process than she ever got in normal living.

Some people feel if they talk about the seriousness of their disease and dying then they will surely die. They say they are "going to beat this illness" throughout the entire course of their disease progression. That may be the attitude of a person who has denied other challenges in their life.

We have a limited control over the time that we die. If there is something we need to do or say that is very important we will try to stay here to complete our work. We've all heard the story of Dad being on death's door. The son coming in from out of town, finally arrives, walks in, and says "Dad I'm here." Fifteen minutes later, Dad dies. He waited for his son to be there.

Or how about waiting by Mom's bedside for days and leaving the room for a second only to return to find she has died. Oh the guilt that goes with that occurrence. It is very important to know, if we are with someone when they die it is because they want us with them. If we are not with someone when they die they chose that also. We can take the gift of love and protection that they have given us. Protective parents tend to not die with their children in the room, even if that child is seventy years old.

Everyone, to some degree, is going to be afraid when it comes time to die. I am a nervous public speaker. It is what I do for a living, but every time I begin a presentation I am frightened. If I am frightened speaking in front of an audience, and I know the outcome will be fine, how will I feel when it comes time to die? I don't remember doing that before. Anytime we do something new we are at least nervous, if not down right terrified.

I'll often hear when a person is talking about end of life issues that they are not afraid to die. As death becomes more of a reality that same person becomes nervous and scared. Their first thought is that they are not strong enough in their religious beliefs, not close enough to their God. If they were they wouldn't be frightened now. The truth is their fear has nothing to do with God but with being a human being facing the unknown. Everyone is going to be frightened as they approach gradual death. It will just be a question of degree.

Most of us are more afraid of the process of dying than of being dead. My belief system tells me that when I am dead I am in a better place. I am not really afraid of being dead. I am afraid of the unknown space between now and the time I am dead.

I have often thought if God would say to me, "Barbara, you are going to die, this is when you're going to die, and how you're going to die," that I would relax, ride more roller coasters, live a freer life.

When a physician says "Go home, put your affairs in order," isn't she really saying, "You're going to die, this is when and this is how?" Unfortunately, most people upon hearing this news go home and sit in their favorite recliner. They might as well die at that moment because they stop living and just wait. Their entire life becomes centered around the disease and dying. They waste precious, valuable time by not living until they are dead.

Months

Two to four months before death from disease occurs, three things start to happen that indicate the dying process has begun. A person's eating habits begin to change, they begin to withdraw from the world around them, and they begin to sleep more and more.

> *It is actually uncomfortable and disruptive for the dying person if we force food and water in the weeks to days before death.*

Months before death from disease, a person's eating habits change. First they will stop eating meat, then fruits and vegetables, then anything that requires energy to digest. Soon they are just eating soft foods. Then in the week or days before death you are coaxing "Please, just a bit of ice cream." Eventually, they are not eating enough calories to sustain their body. Weeks before death they are eating almost nothing.

This is the normal, natural process for us to leave our body. As caregivers we have a terrible time accepting that this is normal. We know that if you don't eat, you don't live. Not eating shows us that indeed death is going to happen. Food also gives us a way of "doing something." We feel helpless but we can make food, even provide favorites. We are doing something. We can show love through food.

Food is the energy we put in our body to make it run. When the body is preparing to die, to stop running, the first thing it does is stop eating. It isn't that the person doesn't want to eat. It's that they can't eat.

When a person is no longer eating enough to maintain life they are also not drinking enough fluids. They become dehydrated. When a person has reached the point in the dying process that they are not eating or drinking enough water they are weeks to days from death.

During this time I often hear family requesting intravenous (IV) fluids (water given through a needle and tubing in the arm) so dehydration doesn't occur. IV fluids actually create discomfort for a person at this point in the dying process. The body is shutting down. Nothing works right. The lungs aren't processing the air exchange, the blood stream is slowed, and the kidneys aren't working properly. All the fluids from the IV that are going into the body are not being processed and peed out. The fluid then settles in the lungs and death occurs by drowning. Not the gentle death we want for our special person.

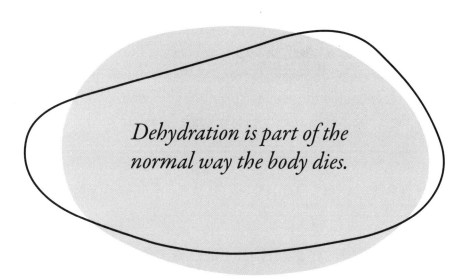

Dehydration is part of the normal way the body dies.

When a person is severely dehydrated the calcium in their blood stream increases. When it gets high enough, you go to sleep and you don't wake up; death comes. **Being dehydrated is the natural way the body dies.** A person gently goes to sleep.

Another part of the natural dying process is a person begins sleeping more. Starting two to four months before death occurs from disease a person begins taking an afternoon nap. This progresses from just an afternoon nap to a morning and afternoon nap. Then to both naps, plus sleeping in front of the TV during the evening. Soon the person is in bed all day, and is asleep more than they are awake.

As family and caregivers we tend to push our loved one to be active, to get out of bed, to stay awake. Our belief, which is true in most of life, is if we don't use our body we will become weaker and less able to function. This is not true for someone who has entered the dying process. We have to change our thinking, new rules apply.

Sleep becomes our friend. Our body is like a battery that is losing its charge. Sleep recharges it. Sleep, like food, buys us a little more energy. It doesn't fix the problem but for awhile it can allow the body to be a little more active.

A nap before and after a planned activity may give a bit more energy to enjoy that activity. As with food there will come a time in the dying process when the body is simply letting go of the need for being awake. It is letting go of its hold on this planet, of its need for the energy that food and sleep provide.

After food and sleep, the third area to look at to see if a person with a life threatening illness has entered the dying process is their social interactions. As food intake deceases and sleep increases our involvement with life's activities and interests begins to recede. Our interest in what goes on around and about us is like a circle that slowly begins to get smaller.

1) First we aren't interested in what is happening world wide: the news, politics, sports. Whatever we had a passion for just doesn't carry our interest like it used to.

2) Then our social circle of friends begins to narrow. We just want to be around those closest to us.

3) As we get even closer to death even our family is too much to converse with or think about.

4) In the weeks before death just being with someone without words is a great comfort. We reach a point where words and thinking outside of ourselves is just too much effort. Our life's work then becomes introspective: thoughts about ourselves, thoughts we keep inside our mind, thoughts that are not for sharing.

This withdrawing is part of the normal, natural way we die from disease or old age. The withdrawing is symbolic of us packing our bag of memories and experiences and building our place in another world. This physical world is no longer where our work is centered. When a person has entered the dying process the gradual decrease in eating, gradual increase in sleep, and slow withdrawal from the world around us are the key points we will monitor to assess how close to death a person is.

No one can put a number on how long a person has to live. The closest anyone can come is months, weeks, days, and hours. Food, sleep, and withdrawal are reliable gauges for a timeline.

Part of the natural dying process is restlessness.
There is an agitation of just not being settled.

Weeks

In the weeks before death from disease there are new changes. I call this period of decline "labor." We go through labor to get into this world and it takes labor to leave it. Think of the little chick that works so hard to get out of its shell. We, too, have to work to get out of our shell, and that usually takes one to three weeks. The key that says this labor has begun is a person sleeping with their eyes partially open. They also may be asleep most of the time, restless, pick at their bedclothes, have random hand movements, and talk while murmuring to themselves.

Sometimes they are alert and responsive to conversation but increasingly are confused and "other worldly." They often talk to, or about, people we don't see, people who have died before them (mothers, fathers, children). There are breathing changes in these weeks before death. A person takes a breath and then stops for an unusual amount of time before resuming regular breathing. I call this "start and stop breathing." It is very common. Also "puffing," a blowing of the lips outward, can be present.

Life becomes more like a dream. We are asleep most of the time. We are also withdrawn, not interested in what is going on around us. As death gets closer and closer we drift further and further away until we don't even respond to anything that is happening around us.

> *Labor is the little chick working to free itself from the shell we call a body. Nothing bad is happening, nothing unnatural is happening. This is how people die.*

These occurrences I've described above tell us that the labor to actively leave the body has begun. Nothing in the body works as it should. It is actively shutting down. The time frame for this activity often depends upon the personality. A Type A personality may have a shorter labor. A person with unfinished business may take longer. The amount of fear a person brings to their life and this final experience can also affect the length and agitation of labor.

Sometimes a person gets to death's door and says, "Wait I'm not ready yet. I have something left undone. Give me just a little longer," and the Universe does.

Days to Hours

When a person is days to hours from death you will see a bluish or a darkened discoloring to the hands and feet (mottling). Their blood pressure will gradually fall to where it can't be heard or seen. The person will be peeing and stooling the bed. Their breathing may increase as well as their pulse. Congestion is often present. How congested a person is will depend on how dehydrated the body is, the more fluids, the more congested. The person is no longer responsive to sound or touch. They can be talking but not making sense, moving, but aimless and unaware of their surroundings.

Hours to Minutes

The key sign alerting us that death will be in hours to minutes is the person begins breathing much like a fish breathes. The mouth opens and closes. Breathing gets slower and slower until it becomes a series of long spaced out breaths. There may be one or two of these breaths or they may continue for hours. I am going to go into detail about the last moments before death because as the life force leaves the body many people are frightened by the unusual occurrence and often carry the particular memory with them forever, complicating their grief.

In the final push to leave the body, there is often a head, shoulder, and/or arm movement. On the face will appear a frown, a grimace, a silent scream. Sometimes there are sounds, sometimes tears, or a tear. Following this movement there will be one or two long spaced out breaths; the rest of the energy is leaving the body. We go through labor to get into this world and we go through labor to leave it. There are so many similarities between birth and death. One is a labor to leave home. The other a labor to return home.

Some women in labor can sneeze and out pops the baby; other women, thirty-six hours later are still trying to push the little one out. So it is with the labor to leave this world. Some of us can get out of our bodies more easily than others.

In the days to hours to minutes before death, the job for us is to look for physical pain, levels of fear (we will all be afraid to some degree), and unfinished business. It is time to say what we need to say from our hearts to the person leaving us, to give our permission to go (not that it is okay to leave us but that we understand it is going to happen), to touch and show our love. These actions can strongly affect the peace that is found in dying. Peace for the witnesses and peace for the dying person.

NOTES

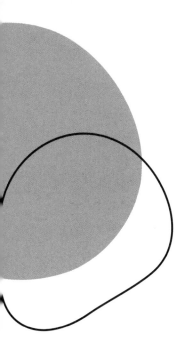

CHAPTER THREE

End of Life Care at Home

We are fortunate when we have someone HELPING US with a life challenge and we are fortunate when we have SOMEONE TO HELP with their life challenge. We all need each other in this world.

Food

When living with a life threatening illness we are eating for two—our physical body and our disease. Nutrition will not keep a person alive indefinitely. It does not stop the disease progression. If we have a terminal illness, the body will eventually die from that disease no matter how much we eat. However, eating may buy a little time.

Once the process of separating from the physical body begins, months before death occurs, rules about nutrition change. When striving for health we follow the rules of low cholesterol, low fat, exercise, regulated caloric intake, low salt, minimal sweets. All these rules can now be forgotten. The focus now becomes high protein and high calories.

If the heart isn't an issue then ignore the rules for a healthy heart. If the pancreas isn't the issue ignore the rules for carbohydrates and sweets. The new rule is eat whatever pleases you, eat often, and start taking a protein supplement drink.

Remember the continuum of withdrawing from foods: meat, fruits and vegetables, puddings, creamed soups, scrambled eggs, ice cream, protein supplement, sips of water. As we move along this continuum the amount of food we eat naturally decreases, so our goal is to provide as much quality nutrition in as little quantity as possible.

Three meals a day is just too much food for a person in the dying process to consume. They become defeated just by looking at "all that food." Six small, high protein, high caloric snacks will go down much better. Let them eat whatever appeals to them but put it to them frequently in the form of small snacks.

Even when the person is still eating a fair amount of good quality food, I recommend beginning to drink some sort of protein supplement. There are plenty of commercial products on the market or you can make your own high protein smoothie. An entire can of protein supplement will gradually become too much. Divide an eight ounce can in half and give the four ounces every two hours from the time the person wakes up until bedtime. That will probably equal four cans. Four cans of three hundred and fifty calories per can is fifteen hundred calories, enough for maintenance if activity is low. The protein supplement every two hours is in addition to the small, frequent, high protein/ high caloric snacks.

There will come a point on the continuum when the protein supplement may be the only nutritional intake. That is okay and very normal. When a person is letting go of their body they don't want the grounding that food brings. Their body sets the pace without them even realizing it. It is okay that they are not eating, but always offer them food. Let the person make the decision to not eat. Again, I stress, part of the normal approach to death from disease or old age is a gradual decrease in food intake.

Eating small meals and drinking high protein will not stop the disease process but you may be buying a bit of time. Eating will not make the disease stronger, while not eating will make the body weaker.

> *Always offer food, but don't force it.*

Water

On the journey toward physical death, as the body stops eating food it also stops drinking water. We all recognize the body's need for water to live. As our loved one stops drinking water we tend to panic and think they should have IV fluids to keep the body "comfortable." Actually, in the days to hours before death the more fluid in the body the more uncomfortable they will be.

When a person has entered the dying process their body begins letting go of its hold on the physical. First food, then water. The entire body is shutting down. As it shuts down it stops functioning normally. The kidneys that process liquids are not performing their job. If you begin IV fluids often times the fluid stays trapped in the body's cells and lungs causing increased discomfort.

The body doesn't want food or water. When a person has entered the dying process and they are not eating any food and not drinking sufficient fluid to keep them hydrated they are a week or so or days from death.

The calcium in their blood will begin to rise because of the dehydration. When the calcium gets high enough a person goes to sleep and doesn't wake up. It is a very gentle, natural way to die.

If left to its own devices the body gives comfort in sleep. A sleep that allows us to leave this world and begin our new journey. This is the normal, natural way to die.

Bowel Movements

Now let's talk about a topic that is often overlooked in medical end of life care: bowel movements. There are major misconceptions about bowel movements in people who can't be fixed, as well as for those who are taking narcotics and/ or non-narcotics for pain.

We often think that when a person is not eating very much they will then not have much to eliminate. That's wrong. Whether we eat or not our body still produces waste, and we will still need to eliminate that waste. Being active helps us poop. The less active we are the more prone to constipation we will be, and people approaching the end of their life have less and less energy with which to be active. Constipation becomes a problem as activity decreases. Laxatives become necessary.

Narcotic and non-narcotic pain medicines slow bodily functions. **This causes constipation which becomes a BIG issue.** Anyone taking medication for pain needs to also be taking a laxative. Pain medicine and laxatives go together, ALWAYS! Don't wait until the person is impacted with three or four days of backed up stool and in great discomfort.

Most people with a life threatening illness need to be assessed for a laxative regime. Of course there are exceptions, the particular disease and the person's bowel history can affect and determine bowel activity, but everyone needs to be assessed. Ninety-nine percent of people on pain medicine will need to also be on a laxative. What kind of laxative? Ask the doctor who prescribed the pain medicine what is recommended. Generally, the stronger the pain medicine the stronger the laxative.

Medical Equipment

When taking care of someone who is ill ordinary household furniture is generally more of a hassle than a convenience. Here are some changes that you may want to consider making, not just to make the person who is very sick more comfortable, but also to help you as a caregiver.

Bed

Most of the mattresses on our beds are comfortable. They are not, however, really made to be in all the time. Beds are generally constructed to be flat and sitting height from the floor. None of that is helpful, it is actually inconvenient, when you are sick or caring for someone who is sick.

Enter the hospital bed. It can be raised and lowered to a desired height (one height for getting out of bed, another height for a caregiver to assist with a bath or changing the sheets). Hospital beds do not have to be in bedrooms. You can put them in the dining room or living room so your special person is not isolated. You can buy or rent a hospital bed. Medicare and some insurance companies pay for them with a physician's order. Ask your physician. There are charities in most states that provide free hospital beds. Even easier, if you qualify for hospice care, a hospital bed is part of the services they offer. Use your favorite internet search engine to find one in your area.

Commode (Portable Toilet)

Getting from the bed to the bathroom can become challenging. You might need a commode which you can move next to the bed and relocate when not in use.

As a person becomes weaker and mobility more difficult you may want to consider a Foley catheter (a tube inserted into the bladder and attached to a bag hooked to the side of the bed so urine can flow into it). It is not painful but may be irritating.

A Foley catheter relieves the stress of having to get out of bed quickly when you need to pee. Keep commode use for bowel movements. As a person becomes less aware of their surroundings, a choice needs to be made between diapers and a foley catheter. Even if a person is only moving their bowels every other day, without a Foley catheter the diapers would have to be changed several times a day.

How to Get Equipment

There are medical supply companies almost everywhere. Check with your insurance provider and/or medicare for coverage.

If your hospital has a Discharge Planner get their assistance as you prepare to go home. If you have home health services ask them about equipment and how you can get what you need. If you are using an EOL Worker they would also be able to help you get what you need. Again, all of this equipment is also provided by hospice.

> *I'm not sure life's goal is really about how many breaths we take but what we can do with the rest of our being while we are taking those breaths.*
>
> *Death is an extension of life. It is our final act of living.*

Also: You might want to consider having several night lights in strategic locations for night checks. A baby monitor allows you to be in other rooms, even sleep in a different area, and still know what is happening.

I strongly recommend you use a hospital bed but if you don't, you need to put a rubber sheet over your mattress to protect it from any number of things. Get bed pads to put between the person's body and the sheet so accidents are removed more easily. As a person becomes less in touch with this world diapers will be necessary. Also, you'll need pillows, lots and lots of pillows. Pillows for putting behind the back, under the knees, between the knees, under the arms. Even with the hospital bed elevated you can use extra pillows under the head. We love pillows; use them everywhere.

Oxygen

Sometimes a person's disease affects their oxygen intake. They have a bluish area around their mouth, a shortness of breath, or they are breathing rapidly. Having difficulty breathing is part of the normal dying process. Having oxygen at home for continual use, or even occasional use, can be beneficial. It probably won't fix the breathing problem but it may make the person a bit more comfortable.

How do you get oxygen into the home? First, you need a doctor's order. Then the doctor's office will contact a company to deliver, set up, and instruct you on how to use the oxygen. The oxygen can be in large cylinders with a gauge and tubing, or be in the form of a concentrator (a machine that converts oxygen in the air into a more concentrated form of oxygen). Tubing runs from the machines to the nose.

Oxygen is very flammable! NO SMOKING in the room, and I would suggest the house. I had a young patient who did not heed that warning, lit a cigarette, and set himself on fire. That story does not end well.

Let's talk a bit about oxygen in the final weeks, days, and hours before death. There is research saying that administering oxygen doesn't prolong life or even have any beneficial effects. It states that the physical body is so compromised due to decreased circulation and lung congestion that there is no effect. The body is shutting down so it can't process the oxygen that is being pushed into it.

My opinion? You need to ask why you are thinking about giving the oxygen. Is it because the person looks like they are having difficulty breathing? As death approaches a person naturally has difficulty breathing. There is congestion (depending upon how hydrated they are). There is generalized restlessness. There are the mouth movements that look labored. Often there are unusual sounds as breath goes in and out. These are part of the normal way a body dies. Remember, nothing works right, everything is shutting down. We are watching a "chick getting out of its shell." There is labor involved in getting out of our body.

It is very difficult to see our loved one struggling. We are watching with our hearts and emotions, not our intellects and our minds. When we have knowledge of the dying process, when we can understand that what we are seeing is normal, our mind can tell our heart "nothing bad is happening here, it is sad, but it's not bad."

Now, back to oxygen. What do we have to lose by administering oxygen as end of life approaches? A few dollars to set it up and pay for it, and it probably won't be any help in easing the breathing challenges. We gain the possibility it will bring a bit of ease to the patient. It will surely bring comfort to us. We will feel we are doing something, that we've tried to make our loved one more comfortable. Oxygen at the end of life can be considered a comfort measure.

> *End of life work is not about just taking care of the patient. It is about caring for everyone present.*

Something that seems to be more helpful than administering oxygen in the days to hours before death is to give a small amount of morphine. The morphine can bring comfort by slowing down the number of times a person breathes in and out.

Anger and Frustration

Taking care of someone at home is more than a 9-to-5 job. It is 24/7. Add the emotional connections and personalities (often challenging on a good day) and you have a caregiver with not always positive thoughts. Thoughts of love and sadness are present always, but thoughts of frustration and exhaustion will show themselves periodically.

There is no perfect family or perfect relationship. There are disagreements and dysfunction in every family. That is life.

As much as we love someone, feelings can turn to frustration and even anger as our efforts to care for them are met with road blocks. Because a person is sick does not mean they have leeway to be rude, mean, to yell, to be unreasonable. Way too often the patient becomes the spoiled child that no one wants to correct or discipline and the caregiver becomes the exhausted parent.

Sometimes we have to be honest and direct even when our special person won't appreciate hearing what we have to say. "I know you want to go for a walk with your walker but your body isn't strong enough anymore. Shall we try to get you into the chair instead?"

You may have to gently remind them of their life threatening illness: "This is how things are now, Mom. Let's do the best we can." You don't have to dwell on sickness and weakness but don't agree with denial either: "No, Mom, you won't be going back to your apartment. I'm sorry but the disease isn't going to let that happen." You can be positive and truthful at the same time. Try to be the firm, stable one.

You can be firm yet loving. When they are angry and lash out at you (and that will happen no matter how great the relationship), tell them it is not okay, you understand the frustration, but don't direct it at you. As a caregiver you must take care of yourself or you will not be able to continue to care for your special person. Just because someone we care about will die someday doesn't mean they can have everything the way they want it. What I've seen happen many times is if limits aren't set families reach the point where it is just too much to care for the person at home.

The past is a memory and the future is an idea, only the present is real. Taking care of someone at end of life gives us the opportunity to live in the present, to build a present. By holding onto our anger we are throwing away our chance for a great present with our loved one. Express love, tenderness, and gratitude that this person is in your life today.

What have my loved one and I traded for a day of our lives? Anger, resentment, accusations? Or have we traded this day for togetherness, joy, and good memories? The choice is ours.

You can't control another's feelings or how they respond to you, but you can change the way you interact with them. As death approaches, the person dying does not have the energy or even consciousness to abide by life's social and personal relationship rules. It is up to you to adapt and change how you interact. You can guide the patient in a manner that concentrates on love, togetherness, and appreciation. You can help celebrate their life and your relationship. It is yours to do, not the patient's. If you want love from your special person, you have to be loving. If you want attention from your special person ,you have to give attention. The patient will probably not be able to initiate relationship needs.

Time is the enemy. Always do and say what needs to be said and done, NOW. There may not be another opportunity.

As a person enters the dying process their personality doesn't change. It intensifies. A grouchy, irritable person can become downright mean. An easy going person becomes more laid back and quiet. Look at the person's personality. Has it intensified or actually changed? If there is a personality change consider the possibility of medical issues and drug reactions before deciding the person is just being unpleasant.

I had a teacher once tell me "as long as we are breathing, even if it is doing nothing else but breathing, we are learning something." That said, a purpose is very important as we approach the end of our life. Most of us live as if we are going to live forever - that we have "all the time in the world." If we think about death at all, other people die, not us.

In the months before death, as our body begins shutting down, we know we are dying even if no one tells us directly. "Why bother" thoughts begin to pop up in our mind: "I'm just not interested, I just don't have the energy, why should I do anything, I'm going to die anyway." To help a person live the best they can until their body completely withdraws, find a purpose. It can fill the time of endless "I can't do anything anymore" thoughts.

There will come a time, in the weeks before death, when our purpose is no longer important. Now begins the work of the "chick getting out of its shell," releasing from a no longer functioning body. But before that happens a project is helpful. That project can be organizing scrapbooks, recording a family history, making phone calls to friends, or an easy craft project. This can fill the time and give you a reason to get out of bed in the morning.

Family Dynamics

Families are a unique grouping of people and personalities. They present us with great opportunities for learning how to get along with others. This seems to go smoothly with some, others, not so much.

What I have discovered is that a family member dying can bring a family together. It can be their finest moment of closeness and comfort. But for other families it brings out the worst in relationships and will affect family dynamics for years. Under stress, emotions seem to bring us together or push us further apart.

There is no perfect family or perfect relationship, no family that never has a disagreement, argument, or misunderstanding. It is natural to have moments of tension and disagreements but we generally work through those moments. This is how normal family relationships work.

Blended/step families take the challenges of getting along to a new level. Habits and history are missing. There is no foundation to draw from and in many cases integration just doesn't happen.

I think relationships and interaction with others are hard work on a good day. Under stress, it is like holding a magnifying glass to the sun. A family member dying is one of the ultimate stressors.

During the illness and dying process, if the family dynamic has been one of support and comfort then there will be more comfort and more support. The magnifying glass effect will increase the family bond. If the relationship history has been one of discord then that discord will likely increase, UNLESS members make a concentrated effort to have a truce.

Care Plan

Taking care of someone 24/7 is a HUGE job. Added to our normal routines is the responsibility of caring for someone who is not just ill but approaching the end of their life. The emotional weight of that responsibility, plus the fear of what death will look like and how it will come, can be overwhelming. Just remembering day to day incidents and information is daunting. Let's explore the areas you need to keep track of on a daily basis and how to do that.

NOTES

DAILY CARE PLAN
Date: _____

Water Intake: _____ ounces

Food Intake
Breakfast: _____
Lunch: _____
Snack: _____
Dinner: _____
Snack: _____

Protein Supplements (8 ounce cans)
1   2   3   4

Peed   1   2   3   4
5   6   7   8   9

Catheter Bag Emptied
Time: _____   How much: _____
Comments: _____
_____

Bowels   1   2   3   4
Comments: _____
_____

Mental Status: Alert   Confused
Comments: _____
_____

Emotional Status: Quiet   Withdrawn
Comments: _____
_____

I smiled today because _____
_____

I am thankful for _____
_____

Activity: Up/About _____
                In Chair _____
                In Bed _____

Sleeping: During the Night _____
                Naps _____
                Sleep Quality _____

PAIN ASSESSMENT   Yes   No
If yes, rate a scale of 1-10: _____
Time of last pain medication _____
In 45 minutes, was there comfort? Yes   No
Pain number then?   Yes   No

Additional Instructions to Plan of Care: _____
_____

Questions for Nurse, Social Worker, Chaplain,
Home Health Aide? _____
_____

Comments About the Day: _____
_____

Today I did this just for me: _____
_____

MEDICATIONS
Medication   Times to Give
_____   _____
_____   _____
_____   _____
_____   _____
_____   _____
_____   _____
_____   _____

Guidance for Filling Out the Daily Care Plan

Intake: Food and water: Recording how much your special person eats and drinks in twenty-four hours is very important. It helps you and your home health team know where on the approaching death timeline they are: months, weeks, or days. Seeing everything written down shows us what food, if any, the person is interested in eating. We can notice the likes and dislikes as well as the qualities of food being eaten. It allows us to make adjustments based on past performance. With that knowledge we can adjust what we are offering and maybe get more calories into the diet.

Output: Tracking urine output is important to see how well the kidneys are working. You don't have to measure how much. Just record how many times a day a person pees and if there is a color and smell change. As death approaches and the person is drinking less, urine often becomes darker and stronger smelling.

Our body makes waste whether or not we eat so we need to monitor bowel movements. They are affected by both eating less and lack of activity. It becomes uncomfortable if a person goes more than two days without pooping. Recording each day allows you to keep track and to notify your home health care team if a laxative is needed.

Mental Status: Is our person confused or alert? It is important to understand that as death gets closer a person goes within, and can become confused, quiet, or forgetful.

Emotional Status: Are they withdrawn, crying, giddy, sad?

Activity: Are they up and about? Do they stay in bed? Can they get out of bed without help?

Sleeping: Is there an afternoon nap? Or a morning and an afternoon nap? Are they asleep more than awake? Again, these are important sign posts. Dying from old age or disease has a process to it. We are monitoring the process as well as recording pertinent information to relay to the health care team.

Pain Assessment: Use a scale of 0 to 10 to assess daily pain. It is not uncommon for there to be no pain. Just because death is approaching does not mean the person will experience pain BUT check each day.

Additional Instructions to Plan of Care: Use this part of the Care Plan sheet to write down care instructions. This is so you are reminded as you go over the sheets what you are to do. With all the tasks on your plate you need reminders. Don't rely on your memory. There is too much on your mind. Write notes, write notes, write notes. This Care Plan has everything in one place for reference when you and your care team need it. Take all of this with you to your doctor's visits. You may not need it, but you have it if you need it.

Questions: Remember to not rely on your memory to retain anything. Use this area to write any questions you may have for your doctor and/or the health-care team.

Comments for the Day: Whatever pops into your mind about the day.

Medications: Again, don't rely on memory. Write things down. Record the medications and the times they are given. You can cross them off and make comments after they are taken. This way there is no forgetting. At the end of the day you can see if everything was given or why it wasn't.

I have included care plan recording sheets at the end of this guidebook for you to use. Go to our website for free downloads when you need more sheets.

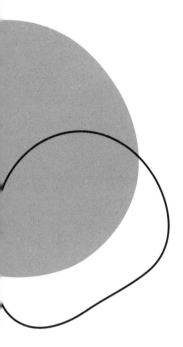

CHAPTER FOUR

End of Life Pain Management

We must look at the person's disease history to evaluate their pain status. Dying is not painful. Disease causes pain. If pain has not been an issue during the disease process then just because a person is actively dying (months, weeks, days, or hours before death) does not mean they are in pain.

If pain has been an issue during the disease process then pain is present to the last breath. Just because a person is not responding does not mean that pain is gone. Whatever is causing the pain is still in the body. When a person is days to hours from death they are not in touch with their physical body in the same manner as a healthy person. You might say they are shedding their body, and the physical sensations are not the same as they would be if the person were healthy. Pain management is different because the body is not functioning normally. Circulation, breathing, and oxygen exchange are not happening properly so medications are not being absorbed and carried throughout the body in a normal way. Nothing in the body works "right," so medications won't work "right" either.

Often dying looks painful to the people watching. Dying is a struggle to get out of the body. There are sounds that ordinarily would indicate discomfort but, when a person is actively dying, are part of the struggle. Just as the little chick works to get out of its shell, a person works to get out of their body. It takes effort to release from our body. That includes rattling and gasping sounds, twitching, random hand and leg movements, picking the air, facial grimaces, and talking that doesn't make sense. All of this is part of the natural struggle to get out of the body. Nothing bad is happening, nothing that isn't normal. This is how people die.

The things I have described in the paragraphs above are generally interpreted as expressions of pain, unless someone tells us differently. That is where health care professionals can give important guidance IF they understand the normal, natural way people die. Sad to say, all too often, health care professionals don't.

If pain has not been a part of a person's disease process then they are probably not in pain now. Dying is not painful, disease causes pain.

There is much confusion and fear regarding end of life pain medicines, morphine in particular. I have made a simple and short list of the major issues. You can use it as a guideline when your loved one is receiving a narcotic.

• To be effective, pain medicine needs to be given on a regular, around the clock, schedule. DO NOT skip the next dose just because your person is comfortable. Pain medicine doesn't make the pain go away it just "covers" the pain up. We must keep the "cover" on.

Morphine must be given around the clock to keep a person relaxed and comfortable.

1) Over time, the original dosage may have to be increased.

2) Everyone's pain is different so everyone's pain medicine and dosage will be different.

3) There is no standardized medicine dosage for pain. It takes time to find the correct pain medicine and the correct amount.

4) The biggest fears about taking narcotics for pain management are of addiction and overdosing.

5) Most medicines given by mouth can be given rectally. Some pain medicines can be made into creams and rubbed on the skin.

6) Generally, there isn't a need for needles in end of life pain management.

7) Pain doesn't stop when a person is non-responsive. Continue the pain management schedule until death.

8) DO NOT crush time released narcotics. They are made to slowly release an appropriate dose of narcotic on a timely basis. If you crush the medicine, you negate the time release part of the pill. ALL of the narcotic will be released into the body at once. This can be too much. It leads to an overdose and possibly death.

9) If you determine there is pain, even though there is no disease history of pain, that doesn't mean you have to jump right into using a hard core narcotic. Ibuprofen may be enough to bring comfort. Narcotics should not be our first line of pain management anywhere in the disease process. That said, there are always exceptions.

10) In end of life care, we just can't make one size fits all statements. We have to observe and make decisions about each person, about their disease, and about how they are responding and reacting within their disease.

NOTES

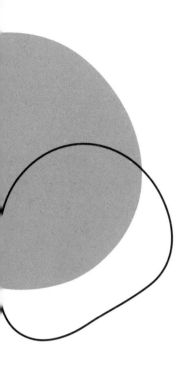

CHAPTER FIVE

Dementia

Dementia is considered a terminal illness in that once you are diagnosed with it, you will die with it. But you won't necessarily die because of it. You may die from heart disease or cancer or something else. Dementia doesn't play by the rules of approaching death affecting eating, sleeping, and socialization. Someone with dementia does not follow the process of a gradual death. They do not show us the signs that death is approaching.

Someone with dementia can withdraw from this world's activities for years. They are not interested, non-interactive, uncomprehending, and unfocused. Someone with dementia can begin sleeping more, or even sleep all the time, and not have entered the dying process. Again, they don't play by the rules.

The only sign that we can use for determining the closeness of death for someone with dementia is their eating habits. When a person is not taking in enough calories (under 1200 to 1500) whether because of difficulty swallowing, forgetting how to swallow, refusing food, or choking, then they are entering the dying process.

If we don't eat we can't live. If the decision not to insert a feeding tube is made then the dying process starts. ALWAYS, ALWAYS offer food. You don't just one day stop feeding someone.

Generally, at this point, the person is struggling against eating. We are the ones concerned. The person's body has already begun to shut down and is probably disliking food. Offer, but don't plead. Also, beware of choking.

When a person is not eating, or not taking in enough calories to sustain the body, you will see all the other signs of approaching death that occur from old age and other diseases. Now the person will fit into the normal timeline that effects others as death approaches.

> *The key question about pushing eating, sleeping, and forcing activities, is what are we trying to accomplish and why? What is the outcome we are hoping for? Notice if by forcing the person to eat and get out of bed they are complying gently or are they unhappy and discontent. If they are displaying unhappiness and discontent why would we want to make their days miserable?*

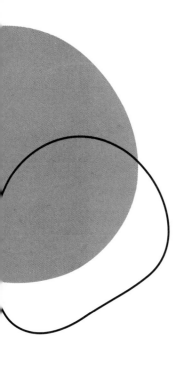

CHAPTER SIX

Caregiver Self-Care

During this time of crisis in your life, it is hard to remember to take care of yourself. Before we can give OF ourselves we first have to give TO ourselves. As caregivers, we tend to put others' needs before our own. If we don't at least try to "put our oxygen mask on first" we will not be able to give the best we can to our special person.

Be Gentle With Yourself

What do I mean by being "gentle" with yourself? Many things! I mean forgive yourself for all the things you feel guilty about, the things you can't do that you want to do, and the things you want to change and can't change.

Remember, we always do the best we can. In hindsight, with more information, we may wish we had done things differently. In the moment, we do the best we are able to do. No one sets out to do something badly.

Being gentle with yourself is also forgiving yourself. Being gentle with yourself is not forgetting your needs and your well being as you provide care and support for someone else. What makes you feel good? What do you need right now?

Being gentle with yourself is not judging yourself for the past but moving forward with positive intentions.

> *One of the best secrets of a happy life is the art of extracting comfort and sweetness from every circumstance.*
>
> *—Thomas Mitchell*

Laughter Heals

Laughter heals physically, emotionally, mentally and even spiritually. Whoever said "All work and no play makes Jack a dull boy" was right. It also makes Jill a dull girl, not only dull in personality but in spirit.

All work diminishes our "light," so we need to purposely feed our spirit with joy. Finding joy enables us to balance and keep in perspective the non-joyful aspects that life is bringing.

Taking on the Distress

As caregivers, we see someone else's pain, stress, and challenges on a daily basis. Part of the challenge in giving care is to not identify with our special person's burden. Sadly, it is theirs to carry, not ours. Our job is to support, care for, and guide.

Adequate Rest

Caring for someone at home is 24/7, and the "goblins" always come out at night. As the ending of life draws closer the question becomes when do you, the caregiver, sleep? Anytime you can! When your special person sleeps, you sleep.

When they are sleeping you may think "Now I can get something done. Now I can do the laundry, do the dishes." My hope is you will assess your personal care before you jump into "things I have to do." Instead ask yourself: "Am I tired? Do I have to do the laundry? What do I really want to do—read, watch a TV show, call a friend, go to sleep?" Your special person's sleep time becomes your time. The trick is to use it wisely.

Getting Out and About

Distancing from your role as a caregiver brings new energy. Get out of the house with a friend. If you're using hospice, have the hospice volunteer stay with your special person while you leave the house. A day out, or at least several hours out, will allow you to return to your responsibilities with a cleared mind and heart.

> *We delight in the beauty of the butterfly, but rarely admit the changes it has gone hrough to achieve that beauty.*
>
> *—Maya Angelou*

Accept Help!

Support from others is the key to getting through this. You don't have to do this alone. Have adult children and relatives, church groups, friends, hospice volunteers be part of your care team—care for the patient and care for you.

In the months before death, when conversations are still being exchanged, schedule time for friends to visit. As physical conditions change, in the weeks before death, those same friends can now just sit and be a presence rather than have conversations. During these visits you can leave the house or just go into another area of the house, but they will give you time to yourself to do what you want.

> *The ultimate lesson all of us have to learn is unconditional love, which includes not only others but ourselves as well.*
>
> *—Elizabeth Kubler-Ross*

Find a Listener

The need to have a safe person to talk with about your feelings and fears is important. Find one person who will be a listener and each day "download" with them. Remember, not just anyone can be a good listener or will have the aptitude to understand. Choose your listener with care. You don't need someone to tell you what to do or even how to do something. You need someone to support and listen to you without judgement and with infinite patience.

Nutrition

Stress eating, sweets, or not eating, are all stumbling blocks in taking care of ourselves. Taking care of someone is stressful. Some of us will unconsciously soothe ourselves with food, and it's generally the wrong kind of food.

Since you are adapting a new eating schedule for your patient (small, frequent, high protein meals—really snacks) you could do the same for yourself. Instead of making one smoothie, make two. Instead of one small high protein snack, make two. If you give a half a can of high protein supplement, drink the other half.

In the early months of the illness you can eat your snacks together, talk and relax. As the dying process advances and it is harder to get your special person to eat, you must eat even when they don't. For awhile, but not indefinitely, your eating with them encourages their eating—even a few bites.

Eating good food is a great goal, BUT sometimes you just have to have that ice cream or whatever you are craving—do it, enjoy it, no recriminations, then go back to eating well.

Write Everything Down

Don't rely on memory. That's why I included the worksheets.

Emotions, Pre-Grief

From the moment of diagnosis, grieving begins. It is not necessarily out in the open but it does live under the surface. It is a sad, uneasy, "if someone looks at me funny I may cry" feeling or even a "if someone doesn't look at me funny I may cry." Some days the feelings are more prominent than other days. Just know this is normal.

> *Experience is not what happens to you, it is what you do with what happens to you.*

At the End of the Day

Create an end of the day ritual. You want a ritual that releases the stress, worry, and concerns. You are caring, loving, doing the best you can in a challenging situation. You want to end each day "clean" so you can move forward into the night and the next day shining.

Take an evening shower. Before you get out of the shower, in your mind's eye, wash all the day's energy and happenings down the drain. Imagine the water beginning at your head and taking all of the day with it as it glides over your body and down the drain. See yourself as sparkling as you step out of the shower.

Before you go to sleep ask yourself what was good about the day. As you tuck your special person into bed for the night you both might share with each other what was good about the day. Find some good. Maybe it was watching the squirrels in the trees, or hearing each other laugh. Find some good before you close your eyes.

The Gift

Being a caregiver for someone you love as the end of their life approaches is a gift you are giving them. In giving this gift you are doing the best you can with the knowledge you have. Most of us know little about caring for the sick, let alone the dying. If you add emotions, fear, and lack of knowledge, this gift of love and devotion can become very heavy.

Please remind yourself each night that you are doing the very best you can with the tools that you have. You are there. You are caring. You are showing the love, and if not the love, then the respect, and if not the respect, then the duty, you feel for someone who has touched your life. Good for you!

NOTES

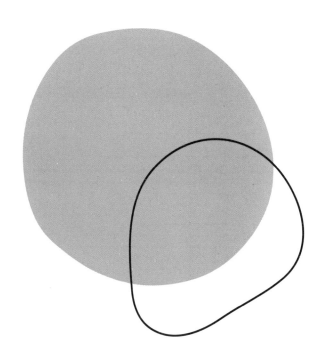

Epilogue

James Dillet Freeman wrote a book years ago titled, **Love, Loved, Loving**. In the book he tells the story of a King who dies and upon his death meets an Angel who invites him to reflect on his life. The Angel asks the King to describe the legacy that he left behind: what does the King think were his three most important achievements?

The King proudly lists his successful stewardship of his kingdom, the vast wealth he built up in the palace coffers, and the adoration he enjoyed from his subjects. These three achievements, in his opinion, comprise a legacy that any man would be proud of!

But the Angel is of a different opinion. While he agrees that these were indeed impressive achievements, they were not the things that truly defined the King. In the eyes of the Angel, the three actions that comprise the King's legacy are: making love to his wife in the moonlight, sitting with his dying cat at the hearthside, and playing with his grandchild even though he had other important matters to attend to.

Before bed each night I ask myself what have I traded a day of my life for. Yesterday I traded a day of my life to enjoy a bright shining moon coming in my window, for playing a couple of hours with a three year old and visiting with a friend I hadn't seen in a while. I think it was worth the trade.

Caring for someone as they approach the end of their life is a legacy-creating moment. My wish for you is that this challenging journey will become part of that legacy the Angel was looking for.

Barbara

DAILY CARE PLAN
Date: _____

Water Intake: _____ ounces

Food Intake
Breakfast: _____
Lunch: _____
Snack: _____
Dinner: _____
Snack: _____

Protein Supplements (8 ounce cans)
1   2   3   4

Peed 1   2   3   4
5   6   7   8   9

Catheter Bag Emptied
Time: _____ How much: _____
Comments: _____
_____

Bowels   1   2   3   4
Comments: _____
_____

Mental Status: Alert   Confused
Comments: _____
_____

Emotional Status: Quiet   Withdrawn
Comments: _____
_____

I smiled today because _____
_____

I am thankful for _____
_____

Activity: Up/About _____
    In Chair _____
    In Bed _____

Sleeping: During the Night _____
    Naps _____
    Sleep Quality _____

PAIN ASSESSMENT   Yes   No
If yes, rate a scale of 1-10: _____
Time of last pain medication _____
In 45 minutes, was there comfort? Yes   No
Pain number then? Yes   No

Additional Instructions to Plan of Care: _____
_____

Questions for Nurse, Social Worker, Chaplain,
Home Health Aide? _____
_____

Comments About the Day: _____
_____

Today I did this just for me: _____
_____

MEDICATIONS

Medication	Times to Give
_____	_____
_____	_____
_____	_____
_____	_____
_____	_____
_____	_____

DAILY CARE PLAN
Date: _____

Water Intake: _____ ounces

Food Intake
Breakfast: _____
Lunch: _____
Snack: _____
Dinner: _____
Snack: _____

Protein Supplements (8 ounce cans)
1   2   3   4

Peed   1   2   3   4
5   6   7   8   9

Catheter Bag Emptied
Time: _____   How much: _____
Comments: _____
_____

Bowels   1   2   3   4
Comments: _____
_____

Mental Status: Alert   Confused
Comments: _____
_____

Emotional Status: Quiet   Withdrawn
Comments: _____
_____

I smiled today because _____
_____

I am thankful for _____
_____

Activity: Up/About _____
                 In Chair _____
                 In Bed _____

Sleeping: During the Night _____
                 Naps _____
                 Sleep Quality _____

PAIN ASSESSMENT   Yes   No
If yes, rate a scale of 1-10: _____
Time of last pain medication _____
In 45 minutes, was there comfort? Yes   No
Pain number then?   Yes   No

Additional Instructions to Plan of Care: _____
_____

Questions for Nurse, Social Worker, Chaplain,
Home Health Aide? _____
_____

Comments About the Day: _____
_____

Today I did this just for me: _____
_____

MEDICATIONS
Medication   Times to Give
_____   _____
_____   _____
_____   _____
_____   _____
_____   _____
_____   _____
_____   _____
_____   _____

DAILY CARE PLAN
Date: _____

Water Intake: _____ ounces

Food Intake
Breakfast: _____
Lunch: _____
Snack: _____
Dinner: _____
Snack: _____

Protein Supplements (8 ounce cans)
1   2   3   4

Peed   1   2   3   4
5   6   7   8   9

Catheter Bag Emptied
Time: _____   How much: _____
Comments: _____
_____

Bowels   1   2   3   4
Comments: _____
_____

Mental Status: Alert   Confused
Comments: _____
_____

Emotional Status: Quiet   Withdrawn
Comments: _____
_____

I smiled today because _____
_____

I am thankful for _____
_____

Activity: Up/About _____
                      In Chair _____
                      In Bed _____

Sleeping: During the Night _____
                      Naps _____
                      Sleep Quality _____

PAIN ASSESSMENT   Yes   No
If yes, rate a scale of 1-10: _____
Time of last pain medication _____
In 45 minutes, was there comfort? Yes   No
Pain number then?   Yes   No

Additional Instructions to Plan of Care: _____
_____

Questions for Nurse, Social Worker, Chaplain,
Home Health Aide? _____
_____

Comments About the Day: _____
_____

Today I did this just for me: _____
_____

MEDICATIONS
Medication   Times to Give
_____   _____
_____   _____
_____   _____
_____   _____
_____   _____
_____   _____
_____   _____

DAILY CARE PLAN
Date: _____

Water Intake: _____ ounces

Food Intake
Breakfast: _____
Lunch: _____
Snack: _____
Dinner: _____
Snack: _____

Protein Supplements (8 ounce cans)
1   2   3   4

Peed 1   2   3   4
5   6   7   8   9

Catheter Bag Emptied
Time: _____ How much: _____
Comments: _____
_____

Bowels   1   2   3   4
Comments: _____
_____

Mental Status: Alert   Confused
Comments: _____
_____

Emotional Status: Quiet   Withdrawn
Comments: _____
_____

I smiled today because _____
_____

I am thankful for _____
_____

Activity: Up/About _____
In Chair _____
In Bed _____

Sleeping: During the Night _____
Naps _____
Sleep Quality _____

PAIN ASSESSMENT   Yes   No
If yes, rate a scale of 1-10: _____
Time of last pain medication _____
In 45 minutes, was there comfort? Yes   No
Pain number then?   Yes   No

Additional Instructions to Plan of Care: _____
_____

Questions for Nurse, Social Worker, Chaplain, Home Health Aide? _____
_____

Comments About the Day: _____
_____

Today I did this just for me: _____
_____

MEDICATIONS

Medication	Times to Give
_____	_____
_____	_____
_____	_____
_____	_____
_____	_____
_____	_____
_____	_____

DAILY CARE PLAN
Date: _____

Water Intake: _____ ounces

Food Intake
Breakfast: _____
Lunch: _____
Snack: _____
Dinner: _____
Snack: _____

Protein Supplements (8 ounce cans)

1   2   3   4

Peed   1   2   3   4
5   6   7   8   9

Catheter Bag Emptied
Time: _____   How much: _____
Comments: _____
_____

Bowels   1   2   3   4
Comments: _____
_____

Mental Status: Alert   Confused
Comments: _____
_____

Emotional Status: Quiet   Withdrawn
Comments: _____
_____

I smiled today because _____
_____

I am thankful for _____
_____

Activity: Up/About _____
               In Chair _____
               In Bed _____

Sleeping: During the Night _____
               Naps _____
               Sleep Quality _____

PAIN ASSESSMENT   Yes   No
If yes, rate a scale of 1-10: _____
Time of last pain medication _____
In 45 minutes, was there comfort? Yes   No
Pain number then?   Yes   No

Additional Instructions to Plan of Care: _____
_____

Questions for Nurse, Social Worker, Chaplain,
Home Health Aide? _____
_____

Comments About the Day: _____
_____

Today I did this just for me: _____
_____

MEDICATIONS
Medication   Times to Give
_____   _____
_____   _____
_____   _____
_____   _____
_____   _____
_____   _____
_____   _____

DAILY CARE PLAN
Date: _____

Water Intake: _____ ounces

Food Intake
Breakfast: _____
Lunch: _____
Snack: _____
Dinner: _____
Snack: _____

Protein Supplements (8 ounce cans)

1   2   3   4

Peed   1   2   3   4
5   6   7   8   9

Catheter Bag Emptied
Time: _____   How much: _____
Comments: _____
_____

Bowels   1   2   3   4
Comments: _____
_____

Mental Status: Alert   Confused
Comments: _____
_____

Emotional Status: Quiet   Withdrawn
Comments: _____
_____

I smiled today because _____
_____

I am thankful for _____
_____

Activity: Up/About _____
             In Chair _____
             In Bed _____

Sleeping: During the Night _____
             Naps _____
             Sleep Quality _____

PAIN ASSESSMENT   Yes   No
If yes, rate a scale of 1-10: _____
Time of last pain medication _____
In 45 minutes, was there comfort? Yes   No
Pain number then?   Yes   No

Additional Instructions to Plan of Care: _____
_____

Questions for Nurse, Social Worker, Chaplain,
Home Health Aide? _____
_____

Comments About the Day: _____
_____

Today I did this just for me: _____
_____

MEDICATIONS
Medication   Times to Give
_____   _____
_____   _____
_____   _____
_____   _____
_____   _____
_____   _____
_____   _____

DAILY CARE PLAN
Date: _____

Water Intake: _____ ounces

Food Intake

Breakfast: _____

Lunch: _____

Snack: _____

Dinner: _____

Snack: _____

Protein Supplements (8 ounce cans)

1   2   3   4

Peed   1   2   3   4

5   6   7   8   9

Catheter Bag Emptied

Time: _____   How much: _____

Comments: _____

_____

Bowels   1   2   3   4

Comments: _____

_____

Mental Status: Alert   Confused

Comments: _____

_____

Emotional Status: Quiet   Withdrawn

Comments: _____

_____

I smiled today because _____

_____

I am thankful for _____

_____

Activity: Up/About _____

                 In Chair _____

                 In Bed _____

Sleeping: During the Night _____

                 Naps _____

                 Sleep Quality _____

PAIN ASSESSMENT   Yes   No

If yes, rate a scale of 1-10: _____

Time of last pain medication _____

In 45 minutes, was there comfort? Yes   No

Pain number then?   Yes   No

Additional Instructions to Plan of Care: _____

_____

Questions for Nurse, Social Worker, Chaplain,
Home Health Aide? _____

_____

Comments About the Day: _____

_____

Today I did this just for me: _____

_____

MEDICATIONS

Medication   Times to Give

_____   _____

_____   _____

_____   _____

_____   _____

_____   _____

_____   _____

_____   _____

DAILY CARE PLAN
Date: _____

Water Intake: _____ ounces

Food Intake
Breakfast: _____
Lunch: _____
Snack: _____
Dinner: _____
Snack: _____

Protein Supplements (8 ounce cans)
1   2   3   4

Peed   1   2   3   4
5   6   7   8   9

Catheter Bag Emptied
Time: _____   How much: _____
Comments: _____
_____

Bowels   1   2   3   4
Comments: _____
_____

Mental Status: Alert   Confused
Comments: _____
_____

Emotional Status: Quiet   Withdrawn
Comments: _____
_____

I smiled today because _____
_____

I am thankful for _____
_____

Activity: Up/About _____
                 In Chair _____
                 In Bed _____

Sleeping: During the Night _____
                 Naps _____
                 Sleep Quality _____

PAIN ASSESSMENT   Yes   No
If yes, rate a scale of 1-10: _____
Time of last pain medication _____
In 45 minutes, was there comfort? Yes   No
Pain number then?   Yes   No

Additional Instructions to Plan of Care: _____
_____

Questions for Nurse, Social Worker, Chaplain,
Home Health Aide? _____
_____

Comments About the Day: _____
_____

Today I did this just for me: _____
_____

MEDICATIONS
Medication   Times to Give
_____   _____
_____   _____
_____   _____
_____   _____
_____   _____
_____   _____

DAILY CARE PLAN
Date: _____

Water Intake: _____ ounces

Food Intake
Breakfast: _____
Lunch: _____
Snack: _____
Dinner: _____
Snack: _____

Protein Supplements (8 ounce cans)

1   2   3   4

Peed   1   2   3   4
5   6   7   8   9

Catheter Bag Emptied
Time: _____   How much: _____
Comments: _____
_____

Bowels   1   2   3   4
Comments: _____
_____

Mental Status: Alert   Confused
Comments: _____
_____

Emotional Status: Quiet   Withdrawn
Comments: _____
_____

I smiled today because _____
_____

I am thankful for _____
_____

Activity: Up/About _____
             In Chair _____
             In Bed _____

Sleeping: During the Night _____
             Naps _____
             Sleep Quality _____

PAIN ASSESSMENT   Yes   No
If yes, rate a scale of 1-10: _____
Time of last pain medication _____
In 45 minutes, was there comfort? Yes   No
Pain number then?   Yes   No

Additional Instructions to Plan of Care: _____
_____

Questions for Nurse, Social Worker, Chaplain, Home Health Aide? _____
_____

Comments About the Day: _____
_____

Today I did this just for me: _____
_____

MEDICATIONS

Medication	Times to Give
_____	_____
_____	_____
_____	_____
_____	_____
_____	_____
_____	_____

DAILY CARE PLAN
Date: _____

Water Intake: _____ ounces

Food Intake
Breakfast: _____
Lunch: _____
Snack: _____
Dinner: _____
Snack: _____

Protein Supplements (8 ounce cans)
1   2   3   4

Peed 1   2   3   4
5   6   7   8   9

Catheter Bag Emptied
Time: _____ How much: _____
Comments: _____
_____

Bowels   1   2   3   4
Comments: _____
_____

Mental Status: Alert   Confused
Comments: _____
_____

Emotional Status: Quiet   Withdrawn
Comments: _____
_____

I smiled today because _____
_____

I am thankful for _____
_____

Activity: Up/About _____
In Chair _____
In Bed _____

Sleeping: During the Night _____
Naps _____
Sleep Quality _____

PAIN ASSESSMENT   Yes   No
If yes, rate a scale of 1-10: _____
Time of last pain medication _____
In 45 minutes, was there comfort? Yes   No
Pain number then?   Yes   No

Additional Instructions to Plan of Care: _____
_____

Questions for Nurse, Social Worker, Chaplain, Home Health Aide? _____
_____

Comments About the Day: _____
_____

Today I did this just for me: _____
_____

MEDICATIONS

Medication	Times to Give
_____	_____
_____	_____
_____	_____
_____	_____
_____	_____
_____	_____

DAILY CARE PLAN
Date: _____

Water Intake: _____ ounces

Food Intake

Breakfast: _____

Lunch: _____

Snack: _____

Dinner: _____

Snack: _____

Protein Supplements (8 ounce cans)

1   2   3   4

Peed   1   2   3   4

5   6   7   8   9

Catheter Bag Emptied

Time: _____   How much: _____

Comments: _____

_____

Bowels   1   2   3   4

Comments: _____

_____

Mental Status: Alert   Confused

Comments: _____

_____

Emotional Status: Quiet   Withdrawn

Comments: _____

_____

I smiled today because _____

_____

I am thankful for _____

_____

Activity: Up/About _____

In Chair _____

In Bed _____

Sleeping: During the Night _____

Naps _____

Sleep Quality _____

PAIN ASSESSMENT   Yes   No

If yes, rate a scale of 1-10: _____

Time of last pain medication _____

In 45 minutes, was there comfort? Yes   No

Pain number then?   Yes   No

Additional Instructions to Plan of Care: _____

_____

Questions for Nurse, Social Worker, Chaplain, Home Health Aide? _____

_____

Comments About the Day: _____

_____

Today I did this just for me: _____

_____

MEDICATIONS

Medication	Times to Give
_____	_____
_____	_____
_____	_____
_____	_____
_____	_____
_____	_____
_____	_____

Barbara Karnes Books

MAIL TO: PO Box 822139 • Vancouver, WA 98682
Phone 360-828-7132 • Fax 360-828-7142

www.bkbooks.com
bkbooks@bkbooks.com

PRODUCT TITLE (See Catalog)	LANGUAGE	QTY	$ PER UNIT (See Chart Below)	SUBTOTAL

TOTAL	$
POSTAGE (See Chart Below)	$
SALES TAX (We Collect for Only These States: GA, IL, IN, KS, MI, MN, NC, OH, VA and WA)	$
GRAND TOTAL FOR ORDER (add together Total, Postage, Sales Tax)	$

Pricing & Discounts for Booklets

1 – 9	$3.00 per copy
10 - 99	$2.00 per copy
100 – 249	$1.80 per copy
250 - 499	$1.70 per copy
500 - 999	$1.60 per copy
1,000 - 2,499	$1.50 per copy
2,500 - 4,999	$1.40 per copy
5,000 - 9,999	$1.30 per copy
10,000 - 24,999	$1.20 per copy

Call for Priority Shipping rates. Quantity discounts are applied to individual products. Postage may be adjusted for rate increases. Visit **www.bkbooks.com** for discounts, postage rates not listed, secure credit card orders, new materials, and eBooks. All fees are subject to change without notice.

Postage & Handling

1 copy	$3.00
2 copies	$4.00
3 – 10 copies	$5.00
11 – 25 copies	$6.00
26 – 50 copies	$8.00
51 – 100 copies	$10.00
101 – 250 copies	$18.00
251 – 300 copies	$25.00
301 – 500 copies	$35.00

CONTACT NAME: _____

ORGANIZATION: _____ PO# : _____

EMAIL: _____ PHONE: _____

STREET: _____

CITY: _____ STATE: _____ ZIP: _____

BILLING CONTACT: (IF DIFFERENT FROM ABOVE) _____

STREET: _____

CITY: _____ STATE: _____ ZIP: _____

PAYMENT: ☐ CHECK (Payable to B. Karnes Books) ☐ CREDIT CARD (enter card info below)

CREDIT CARD #: _____

EXP DATE: _____ CVV CODE:_____